Grandma
Cut Her Hair

ISBN 9798409164430
Printed in the U.S.A.

TABLE OF CONTENTS

Chapter 1	My Jordan, My Joy
Chapter 2	Grandma's Dilemma
Chapter 3	Preparing Joy for the Transition
Chapter 4	Jordan's Voice
Chapter 5	The Big Chop
Chapter 6	You're Not My Grandma
Chapter 7	I Love You Grandma

DEDICATION

This book is dedicated to every grandmother who has raised, supported, played a major role and loved their beautiful granddaughter. This book has been lovingly written for my six-year-old, inquisitive, smart and outspoken granddaughter, Jordan "Joy" Lorraine Void.

FORWARD

"Grandma Cut Her Hair," is a true story, about a grandmother's struggle, to let go of something that was no longer healthy for her.

"Grandma Cut Her Hair," recognizes that the "little girl," in each of us, battles not just with hair disorders, but we also battle with other challenges, that make us feel inadequate.

It was during this "hair journey," that Grandma was able to teach Joy agility, resilience, self-worth, self-confidence and self-love.

Grandma's "hair journey" allowed Joy to exercise her "VOICE," and it taught her that "HEALING" has to take place from the inside out. Grandma reminded Joy, that sometimes you have to let go and start all over again.

Chapter 1
My Jordan, My Joy

"WE ARE BEAUTIFUL BEYOND MEASURE!"
Dr. Void

I knew the moment I laid my eyes on Jordan Lorraine Void, there was something very special about her. When Joshua, Jordan's dad, placed Jordan in my arms in the ICU, Jordan instantly earned the nickname "Joy," because of the indescribable "Joy" that I felt the moment I held her.

I was "in love" all over again! As "Joy" quietly rested in my arms, I never imaged her growing up and having a "voice." I believed that Joy would stay cuddly and small forever! As I sat in the ICU, rocking my Joy, all I could think, was that I could not wait until it was time for My Joy to come home. There were so many stories I wanted to tell her, so many songs I wanted to sing to her and a plethora of dances to teach her. Joy had stolen Grandma's heart forever!

“When I first saw you, I said, oh my what a DREAM!”

Jordan began walking and talking at a very young age, despite the fact that she was born prematurely. She never had a problem showing her approval or disapproval even before she was able to form words. When Joy liked something, she would let you know. When she did not like something, she would truly let you know, by turning away from it, or pushing it away.

When Joy entered school, at the age of three, we began noticing how she would easily speak her "truth" to her friends, her teachers and her family. As Joy got older, she began to realize that she had a "voice," and did not hesitate to let you know how she felt about anything, that was going on around her. Joy was able to express her discontent about things she did not care for, for example, her clothes, her teachers, her work, her toys and my appearance.

When the family recognized Joy's strength (her ability to speak her mind), we all worked together to redirect and "massage" the way Joy would say something or respond to us and other people. We did this so that people would not see Joy as rude, disruptive, disrespectful or obnoxious.

As a "village," we decided that we would support the "GIANT" that was growing and developing inside Joy. We directed and re-directed the way she spoke to us, and the way she spoke to other adults and children. The family knew that Joy had a "strength," that would one day be unstoppable, as an African American woman in this 21st century. We knew that we did not want to "kill" the "GIANT" inside of Joy but we also knew that we needed to tame the "GIANT" until it was time to be released in the earth.

"Never let go of your POWER in the PROCESS!"
Dr. Void

Chapter 2
Grandma's Dilemma

“When we give ourselves permission to walk in our own TRUTH, we will realize we have CONQUERED half the battle.”

Dr. Void

For the last seven years, I wore a beautiful head of brown locs. I had been wearing my locs for almost eight years. It was around January 2019, that I began to notice my beautiful brown locs were thinning. It was as if the weight of my long bouncy locs were becoming too heavy for my soft hair. My Loctician Lorraine, was doing everything possible, to support the now noticeably thinning and balding spots in my head.

The styles that Lorraine created for my "crown" were amazing, but after a while, the styles were not able to camouflage the hair thinning and loss that I was experiencing. This made me very self-conscious and I became anxious about the issues concerning my crown.

Joy loved playing "hair stylist" with my locs. She would pretend she was my loctician and she would fashion my locs in tons of lavish styles. This was Joy's time to create beautiful masterpieces with her Grandma's locs. She would spend hours styling my crown. This was all Joy knew, standing on Grandma's bed and playing "hair stylist" with Grandma's hair!

There were moments while Joy was styling my locs, that she would stop and say, "Grandma, what's that in your head?" I would explain to Joy, that Grandma was getting older, and her hair was thinning, so be sure you are very gentle with my hair when you twist it." I explained to Joy that one day I would have to cut my hair and start all over again!

Joy looked at me as if I were speaking a foreign language. She responded by saying, "yeah right!" That's how she would respond if she was not receptive to what was being said. She simply did not engage in the conversation. She would pick up her iPad, and continue playing, as if I never said a word.

Grandma cutting her hair was unheard of to Joy, because all she had ever known was Grandma's beautiful brown locs, that she would hold on to when I carried her. She enjoyed the locs that I would swing back and forth in her face while we played, and the locs that she got a chance to style every time she came to visit Grandma.

"Our CROWN is only five percent of our external BEAUTY!"
Dr. Void

Chapter 3
Preparing Joy for the Transition

“My greatest fear is, “I don’t fear.”
Dr. Void

In June 2019, I decided to, take my locs out, and let my hair breathe. The thinning appeared to be progressing rapidly. I had my Loctician Lorraine, braid or cornrow my hair up to camouflage the thinning areas. It was a shock to everyone, when people saw me the next day without my locs. It was also a shock to Joy to see them come out, because my locs was the only hairstyle she had ever seen on Grandma. Grandma's locs were gone, and she had to get used to seeing me without the hair she could play in!

Even after putting the cornrows in my hair, I still had to explain to Joy that Grandma will probably have to cut her hair off, if the thinning continued. Again, my Joy did not want any parts of the conversation. The word "cut" was not resonating in her mind, because she was not receiving it. She was already upset about my locs being untwisted and she was not ready to accept that there may be nothing for her to play with and style.

September came, and now my crown was showing signs of being unhealthy. I tried everything from changing shampoos, to buying expensive conditioners, to purchasing expensive hair oils.

Nothing was helping my crown. I became stressed out and I thought to myself, I could buy a wig. All I wanted was to have my hair and scalp respond to one product and start looking healthy again.

I was becoming more and more discontented with my crown. I told Joy to get ready because Grandma was going to do it! I decided to cut my hair in the fall, because June, July and August were very busy months. Joy looked relieved and she continued playing on her iPad.

Well September came, then October, and I was still battling with the decision to go and get it cut. I told myself, and my Joy, that I would cut it around Thanksgiving, because I would have some time off. November and Thanksgiving came and left, and my hair still did not get cut! I said to Joy, "Now I will have to wait and go around Christmas, because I will have more time to get it done." Well after all of the shopping and holiday celebrations, you guessed it – I still had not gotten my hair cut!

I contemplated over all of the reasons I needed to cut my hair, so that I would feel great again, but it was just not enough for me to go and get the "Big Chop" done.

We were ringing in the New Year, and by this time I had convinced myself that all I had to do was keep my hair shampooed, oiled and braided and my crown would begin to heal.

"We must learn to laugh in the face of adversity and disappointments!"
Dr. Void

Chapter 4
Jordan’s Voice

"We must be aware of our internal and external BEAUTY even in our own PAIN!"

Dr. Void

In January, my hair started showing more signs of thinning, hair loss and a flakey scalp. I tried a number of expensive products that according to their label, was "proven" to help with hair loss and thinning. I followed the directions, but my hair continued to do the opposite of what the product said it would do. Nothing was working, and I was becoming more and more depressed, because when a woman's crown suffers, her self-esteem suffers.

"Joy," I said as she was playing on her iPad, "Grandma is ready to cut her hair! I can't do this (pointing to my hair) anymore. I'm just going to make my appointment with Phyllis and cut my hair." "Grandma," Joy yells, "You're going to look ugly with your hair cut!"

Wow, I thought to myself, that did not feel good! Was it the word "ugly" that penetrated my heart? For some reason, Joy's comment about me looking ugly, made me feel like someone had found a large red brick, and threw it at my head. I had to regroup and get myself together. "Joy, that was not nice! I would never say that to you!" Realizing that what Joy said, made me feel some kind of way, and all I could do was suck up my feelings, hold back my tears and walk away.

Joy did not show any remorse about what she said to me, nor did it appear as if she was concerned about how she made me feel when she called me ugly.

Was this the "voice" that we knew rested inside of Joy? Was she using this opportunity to try her "voice" out on Grandma? Did we give Joy the "green light" years ago, to speak up and speak loudly when she needed to express herself, and did Joy really want me to feel her disapproval and disappointment, about me wanting to cut my hair?

Wow! My "bold" Joy was using that "voice" that showed up in her, when she was three years old, to say "NO GRANDMA!" My six-year-old granddaughter brought all of her heartfelt thoughts and words together as best as she knew how, to outwardly express how she felt about my decision to cut my locs. I believe that Joy trusted herself, in that space and moment, to exercise her "voice," and say what she needed to say about me cutting my hair.

"There will be moments in life when you will have to choke on your tears, stick your chest out, hold your head up high and keep it moving."
Dr. Void

Chapter 5
The Big Chop

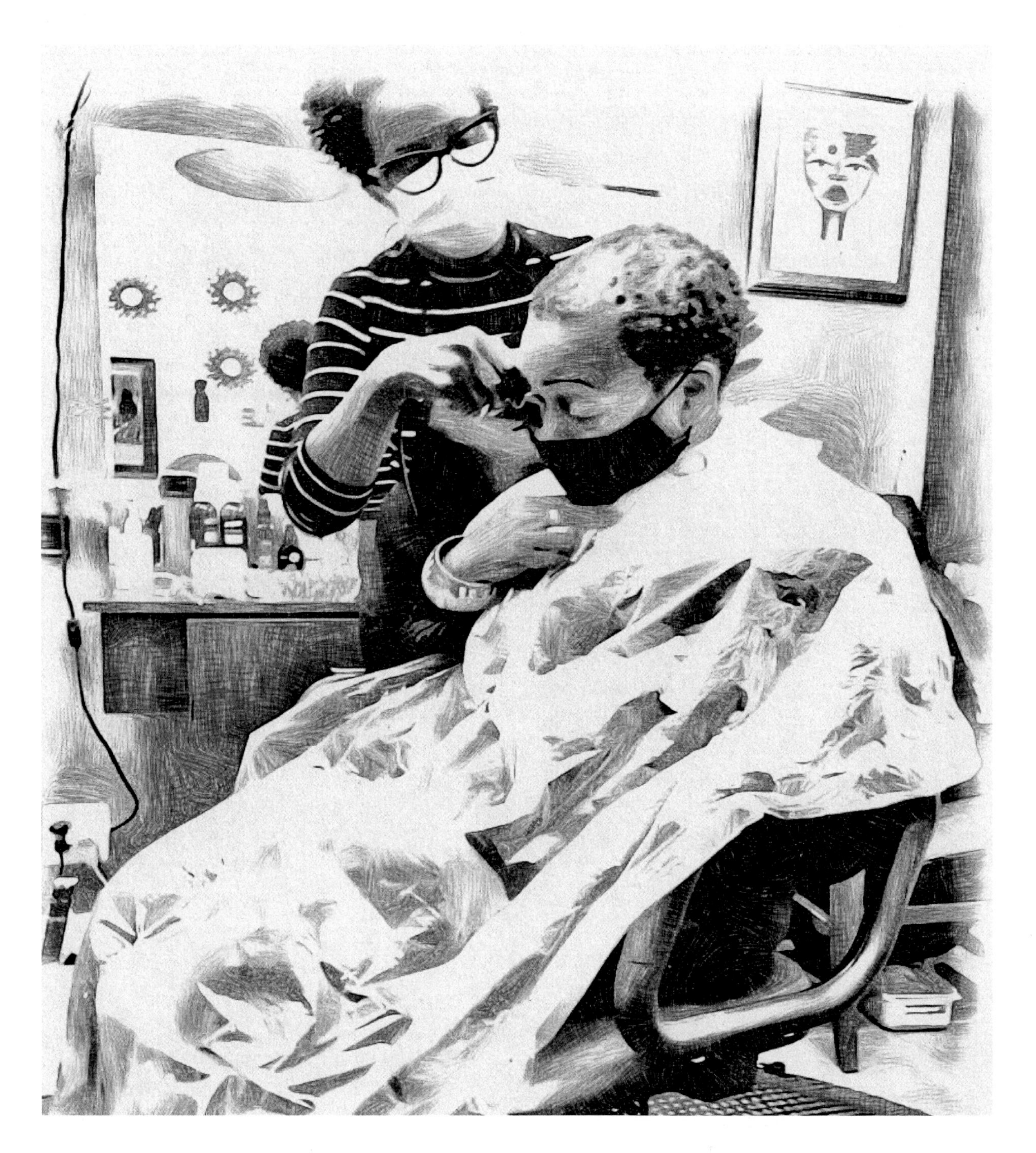

“When we give ourselves permission to LOVE ourselves, even with all of our inadequacies, we WIN!”

Dr. Void

"I love me some me!"
Dr. Void

I took the first step! I made my appointment to cut my hair. I had talked about it and talked about it, and now it was two weeks before the "Big Chop!" I kept reminding Joy each time I spoke to her, that it was almost time for me to get my hair cut. Each time I would remind Joy about my cut, she would just look at me and never say a word. Joy would just keep playing with her iPad or her dolls. She acted as if I never said anything to her.

February 11, 2020 arrived! It was the "Big Chop Day!" I will remember that day for a very long time. When I arrived at the salon, Phyllis seated me in the chair, and she took her time cutting my hair. Section by section, I was letting go all of those negative thoughts and images I had about myself and my hair. My crown was keeping me in "BONDAGE," and my "BONDAGE" was keeping me from being GREAT!

I watched as my hair graced the salon floor. I believe Phyllis cut my hair in sections, so that I would not be traumatized by the whole experience. When I looked in the mirror, and I realized that I did not look like myself, but I LOVED who I was BECOMING, there was a "PEACE" that came over me as she continued to cut my hair! I could feel a "NEW-FOUND FREEDOM" rising up in my soul! I was EVOLVING! I began enjoying the person that my NEW hair cut was creating! I was CONFIDENT again! I was EXCITED again! I was FREE from the bondage that my "sick crown" had me trapped in, and I was being HEALED!

I was so appreciative to Phyllis, for releasing me from the disgrace of hair loss, hair thinning and scalp irritation. Phyllis guided me to the "GREATER IN ME!" I could not wait to take selfies and put them on my social media pages. I wanted to show the world the "NEW" Dr. Lois Void!

I took a plethora of pictures at the salon and at home, and I started posting immediately, so that no one would be surprised when they saw me in person.

"Our BEAUTY resonates from the inside out!"
Dr. Void

Chapter 6
You're Not My Grandma!

“The voice inside of me speaks louder than what the world hears.”
Dr. Void

"If you smile at the universe, it will smile back at you!"
Dr. Void

Elijah, my great-nephew, and his bus drivers, were the first people to see me, with my "NEW CHOP." Elijah is non-verbal, but you could see in his eyes that he was full of questions! He stared at me, from the time he got off of his bus, until his mother came to pick him up. That afternoon was filled with so many emotions, but I endured.

I had so many loves, likes and emojis on my social media pages. I could not keep up with the "Thank You's" that I wanted to send everyone. There were no negative remarks on my pages, and I must say that I was grateful! Post after post, everyone only had beautiful things to say about my "Big Chop!"

Valentine's Day, Friday, February 14th, was also "Fun Friday" for my after-school program. I was on my way to pick up Joy, and all of the other children who participated in the program. Fun Friday was a time when all of the children got together, at Chick-Fil-A, and had a great time eating and playing on the indoor playground! After getting Elijah off of the school bus, I headed to Joy's school.

When I arrived, everyone was shocked to see Grandma with all of her hair cut off. After I signed in, I went downstairs to Jordan's classroom.

I bounced into Jordan's class and told her teacher that I was ready to get her from school. Jordan was in a small group playing with her friends. When she saw me, she stopped in her tracks. Jordan stared at me and turned around and stormed back to her desk! As she stomped away, she blurted out, "You are not my Grandma!"

I could feel water building up in my eyes out of humiliation. The teacher and Elijah were both shocked at the way Jordan had treated me. I could feel myself shrinking in front of everyone, so I said to Elijah, "Let's go, Jordan's mom can come and pick her up."

Elijah and I walked out of the door and started down the hallway. As we were walking down the hallway, I could hear these footsteps moving quickly behind us. I refused to look back, because I was so disappointed, about what I had experienced. I wanted to get out of the building as quickly as possible.

I could see Jordan gathering her belongings quickly, so that she could hurry and catch up to me and Elijah. Jordan must have had an epiphany after we walked out of her classroom, and she realized that her Grandma was serious about leaving her at school, especially after her outburst.

Embarrassed about her Grandma's haircut, Jordan stayed a few feet behind us. She followed me and Elijah to the truck without saying one word. I used my peripheral vision, to make sure Jordan was still with us. I made sure to never turn around and look at her, because I wanted Jordan to see that her Grandma was still proud of who she was and what she had done.

Jordan never caught up to us as we walked to the truck. She was so embarrassed about my appearance, that she kept her distance. I patiently waited for Jordan as she rushed to catch up. Still silent, Jordan boarded the truck.

While driving to pick up the next group of children, Jordan broke her silence and said, “Grandma, can I see your phone?” “Yes,” I said in excitement! Joy is talking to me! I stopped at a red light and handed her my phone. As I began to pull off, Jordan handed me my phone back and said, “This is my Grandma!” Jordan had used my phone to go through my camera roll. She was looking for pictures of me, so that she could show me the woman that she knew as “Grandma.”

Humiliated again, both Jordan and I remained quiet during the next pick-ups, and all the way to Chick-Fil-A.

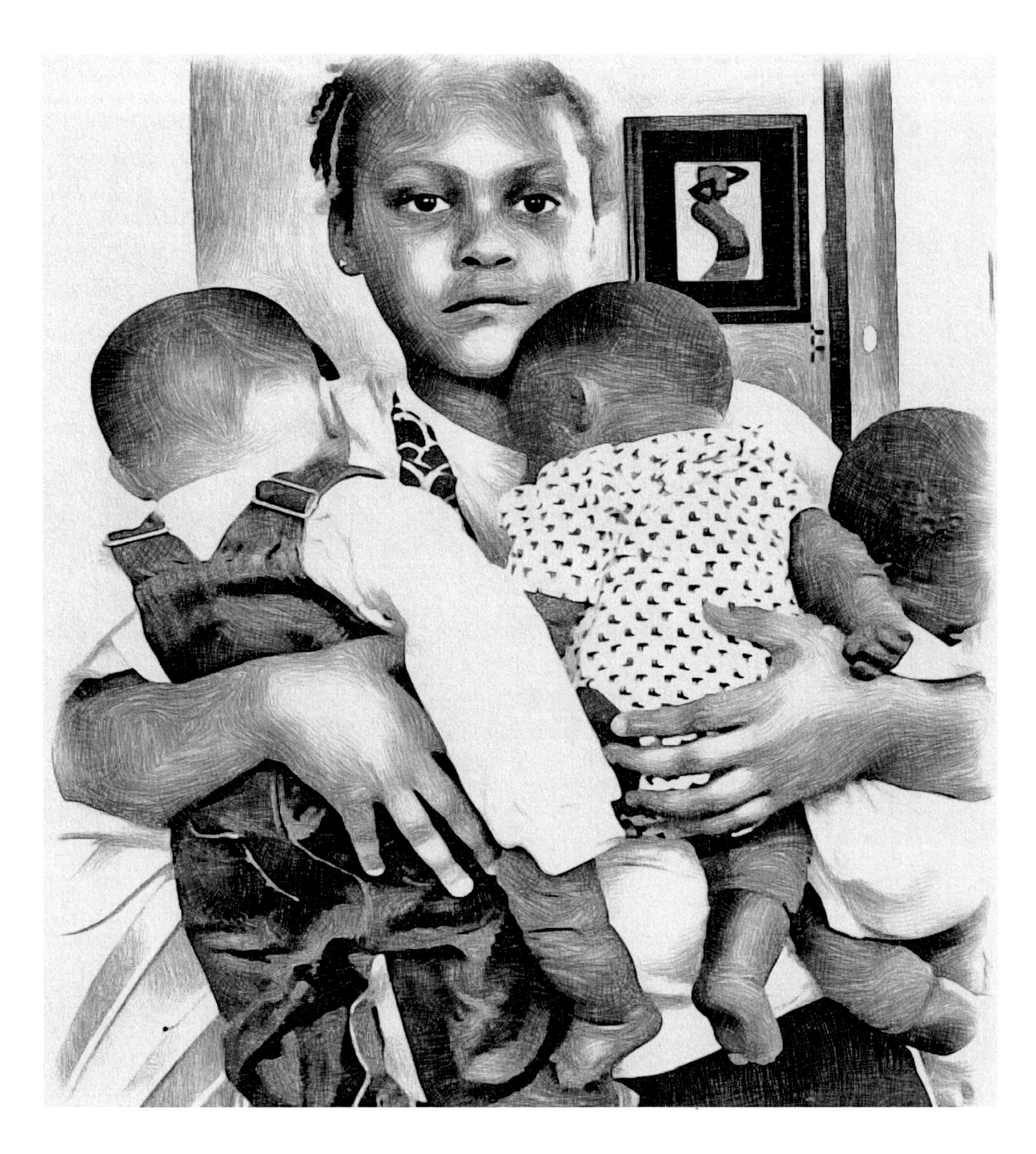

"Unkind actions and words can be overcome with LOVE!"
Dr. Void

Chapter 7
I LOVE YOU GRANDMA

"A grandmother's LOVE has no boundaries."
Dr. Void

I continued picking up the other children from the other schools. As each of them boarded the truck, they each had their very own reaction to my haircut. All of their reactions were totally different from Jordan's, and after saying, "You cut your hair Dr. Void," each child got in and said, "Good afternoon," and they continued talking and playing with each other all the way to Chick-Fil-A. Unbothered about my hair.

While we were sitting down and eating our food, the children would give me a smile and a stare, and say again, "Dr. Void, you cut your hair?" I would say, "Yes," and they would continue eating, laughing and talking.

Joy just nibbled and watched, as each child evaluated my haircut and was unbothered by it. The more she watched and listened to them ask a question, eat their food and laugh out loud, the more she began to realize that no one seemed to care about her Grandma's hair! No one looked at me differently! No one was mean to me because I had decided to cut my locs off! All they saw, was the same Grandma who had "hair," was the same Grandma without "hair!" To the other children, Grandma was still "Dr. Void!"

I could see Jordan letting go of her disappointment, because the children did not care about what her Grandma looked like, as long as she was showing them love. I would watch Joy's expressions as each child would come up to me and play and laugh. Joy quietly examined the way each child talked, laughed, and played with the "hairless" Dr. Void! She was AMAZED at the way they interacted with her "bald" Grandma. Joy had that look of, no one seemed to be bothered with the fact that Grandma cut off all of her hair! All of the children were just loving on her Grandma the same way they did when she had her locs!

As we were preparing to leave Chick-Fil-A, Grandma heard a small voice say, "Grandma, are we getting ready to go or can we keep playing?"

WOW, I thought! Joy called me Grandma! I got filled up and I turned around and hugged my Joy as tight as I could because she finally acknowledged who I was in the midst of my NEW haircut. After three long hours of silence and ignoring me, Joy finally said something to her Grandma!

Hearing Jordan's voice truly lifted my spirit! My soul began to dance from the inside out! The smile on my face stretched across my entire being! I responded to Joy by saying, "Yes Jordan, we are getting ready to leave, but I am giving everyone 10 more minutes to have a GREAT time!"

Jordan ran over to "her Grandma." She kissed me on my cheek and gave me a GREAT BIG HUG! Joy looked at me and said, "I LOVE YOU GRANDMA!" I replied, "I LOVE YOU TOO!"

I said to Joy, "Jordan I'm still Grandma, and I will always be your Grandma! I am Grandma with hair, and without hair! Please know that my hair will never define my LOVE for YOU! Remember, Grandma is BEAUTIFUL from the inside out and we are BEAUTIFUL beyond measure!"

~ The End ~

Epilogue

The relationship between a grandmother and a granddaughter is priceless. Use that time together to impart wisdom that will stay with them for a lifetime. Embrace their "VOICE," allow them to have an opinion and never be afraid to listen to what they have to say, even if it does not make any sense. Last, if you are raising your granddaughter, protect her, guide her and always remind her that no matter what the world may tell her, "She is BEAUTIFUL beyond measure!"

Made in United States
North Haven, CT
30 April 2022